This book belongs to:

_____

My Two Minute Journal

Cover & interior design by Daniel Olexa

Cover photo by GeorgyGirl via Pixabay
Spine image by Pointman2007 via Pixabay
Cover & interior flourish by GDJ via Pixabay

My Two Minute Journal

ISBN: 978-0-578-55886-8

First Edition: August 2019

Copyright © 2019 by Daniel Olexa

Daniel Olexa Hypnotherapy, LLC
P.O. Box 3161
Redondo Beach, CA, 90277
daniel@danielolexa.com
310-746-5929

My Two Minute Journal

Acknowledgements

"If you want to go fast, go alone.
If you want to go far, go together"

~ African Proverb

I would like to thank my friends, family, and those who tested and supported this effort to bring new awareness to the journal genre. Your insights, feedback, and patience made this work more inspiring and powerful.

My deepest thanks to:

Daniel Gutierrez, for your coaching, mentoring, and friendship. Thank you for your inspiration.

Tiffany Cianci, Stephanie Shantz, Erin Laurvick, and Michael Ferrarella for your willingness to share your experiences.

And most importantly, Sarah Richardson, for making every day magical. To the moon and back!

My Two Minute Journal

Welcome to Your Two Minute Journal.

Thank you for choosing this book to help you on your path to a better life through increased focus and awareness of the beneficial lessons and information you experience every day.

At this moment, you may be feeling stuck, like you are beating your head against a brick wall.

I've had clients say that at our first meeting – they're looking to get out of a stressful situation and start being happy.

I've been there myself. I get it.

I've also moved beyond that old unaware self by taking the steps that you'll be journaling as you work with this book.

Why Two Minutes?

Because awareness is tuning into your intuitive nature. You can get there quickly and begin to honor your natural instincts.

You don't necessarily need to dwell in deep thought to align with your intuition. You just need to become aware of it – possibly following your gut more than your head.

We're taught to not follow our instincts at a fairly young age. That sentiment is later reinforced in relationships, friendships, and work interactions throughout our adult lives.

We're told to do what's right for someone else, to not be selfish, to go to a party/meeting/event even though we really don't want to, because it would be rude not to go. Each time we deny our instinct to say no, we lose a little bit of our connection to our higher awareness and intuition.

Two minutes, twice a day is all you need to reconnect and start hearing/feeling your inner awareness come back to life.

If you find that you wish to dive deeper into connecting to your awareness through longer writing assignments, meditation, or other activities, by all means do so. This journal is merely one tool in your arsenal as you grow into your ideal self.

How to Use This Book

You'll notice that the first entry is noted for the evening of the day that you start.

This is intentional.

Yes, most journals will start with the morning – writing your intentions for the day. We'll get there. That's really step 2.

Step one is embracing your subconscious awareness and bring this wonderful storehouse of information to your conscious awareness.

Your subconscious mind is always receiving information, much, much more information than your conscious mind can decipher. Imagine that you have walked into a movie theatre that is playing over 15,000 films. You can only consciously pay attention to one, but your subconscious is aware of them all.

As you sleep, your subconscious is controlling your breathing, your heartbeat, your body temperature, and more…it's also communicating with you through your dreams.

Your dreams are symbolic messages to help you understand the events of your day & life. Each is an opportunity to gain insight into your deeper/higher awareness.

At this moment, you may be saying to yourself, "I never remember my dreams." Well, that may be true, but I also bet that you remember at least one. If you can remember at least one, then that means that "never remembering" is a falsehood.

It also means that when you go to sleep with the intention of being aware of your dreams and their messages, that you will be more likely to awaken with recall of your experiences.

As you fill out the evening pages of this journal, think back on your day and the challenges you may have faced.

Maybe you had a bad day and felt like a failure. We've all been there.

But what if, as Matt Kahn wrote in *Everything is Here to Help You,* these challenges are your greatest opportunities for growth?

Rather than perceiving failure, ask yourself how these events can help you to grow.

Jot down your lessons for the day in the first set of lines.

Of course, lessons are useless if we don't apply them, so the next entry area is for you to bring the learning fully into your conscious awareness and choose how to apply it into your life.

Finally, as you are preparing to go to sleep, consider the last entry area: "What can I do to make tomorrow even better than today?"

This question places you firmly in the driver's seat of your life. YOU can choose to make the day better. You are NOT experiencing life at the whims of fate.

You are in control.

The morning questions are designed to get you focused on noting the awareness you gained while you were sleeping, applying it, and then setting your intention of success for the day.

Notice the active voice in question 3: "What am I going to achieve today?"

This is very intentionally worded as an affirmation of success rather than as a desire or want, for example, "What do I want/wish to accomplish today?"

They seem like similar questions, almost interchangeable, but they are not.

Wanting and wishing are states of desire. We can want & wish but never take action. (Have you ever joined a gym wishing/wanting to get in shape? How many times did you visit before you stopped going?)

By stating this final question as an affirmative assumption of your ability to achieve, you will create a sense of accountability and responsibility for yourself to make things happen.

You may want to take baby steps, or you may want to take giant leaps. Do what is right for you.

If for some reason you do not achieve your intended goal for the day, do not view it as a failure.

Instead, ask yourself, "What did I learn from this experience?" and apply that learning to your evening entries.

That brings us full-circle.

At the end of each week (7 days of journaling) you'll be prompted to review your week and look for themes and repetitious thoughts/events.

Every month, (4 weeks of journaling) you'll be prompted to review the learnings of your previous 28 days.

As you notice recurring themes in your life, particularly those that are keeping you from being fully happy and successful, you will be more in control of your actions as you choose whether to stay in a loop of frustration or to move forward with focus to achieve your goals.

Enjoy your journey forward. You are now taking action – even the seemingly small act of purchasing this book is a step forward.

Use this book, learn and allow your perceived failures to become the lessons they are meant to be.

Grow into your successful self and enjoy your life.

Now it is time for you to begin.

Turn the page and enjoy.

My Two Minute Journal

My
2
Minute
Journal

My Two Minute Journal

Date: _____

Evening:

What was my biggest challenge today?_____

_____

_____

What did I learn about myself from this challenge? _____

_____

_____

How can I apply this lesson in my life?_____

_____

_____

_____

_____

What can I do to make tomorrow better than today?

_____

_____

_____

_____

My Two Minute Journal

Date: _____

Morning:

What did I learn while I slept/dreamed?

_____

_____

_____

_____

_____

How can I apply these lessons in my life?_____

_____

_____

_____

_____

_____

What am I going to achieve today?

_____

_____

_____

_____

My Two Minute Journal

Date: _____

Evening:

What was my biggest challenge today?_____

_____

_____

What did I learn about myself from this challenge? _____

_____

_____

How can I apply this lesson in my life?_____

_____

_____

_____

_____

What can I do to make tomorrow better than today?

_____

_____

_____

_____

My Two Minute Journal

Date: _____

Morning:

What did I learn while I slept/dreamed?

_____

_____

_____

_____

_____

How can I apply these lessons in my life?_____

_____

_____

_____

_____

_____

What am I going to achieve today?

_____

_____

_____

_____

My Two Minute Journal

Date: _____

Evening:

What was my biggest challenge today?_____

_____

_____

What did I learn about myself from this challenge? _____

_____

_____

How can I apply this lesson in my life?_____

_____

_____

_____

_____

What can I do to make tomorrow better than today?

_____

_____

_____

_____

My Two Minute Journal

Date: _____

Morning:

What did I learn while I slept/dreamed?

_____

_____

_____

_____

_____

How can I apply these lessons in my life?_____

_____

_____

_____

_____

_____

What am I going to achieve today?

_____

_____

_____

_____

My Two Minute Journal

Date: _____

Evening:

What was my biggest challenge today?_____

_____

_____

What did I learn about myself from this challenge? _____

_____

_____

How can I apply this lesson in my life?_____

_____

_____

_____

_____

What can I do to make tomorrow better than today?

_____

_____

_____

_____

My Two Minute Journal

Date: _____

Morning:

What did I learn while I slept/dreamed?

_____

_____

_____

_____

_____

How can I apply these lessons in my life?_____

_____

_____

_____

_____

_____

What am I going to achieve today?

_____

_____

_____

_____

My Two Minute Journal

Date: _____

Evening:

What was my biggest challenge today?_____

_____

_____

What did I learn about myself from this challenge? _____

_____

_____

How can I apply this lesson in my life?_____

_____

_____

_____

_____

What can I do to make tomorrow better than today?

_____

_____

_____

_____

My Two Minute Journal

Date: _____

Morning:

What did I learn while I slept/dreamed?

_____

_____

_____

_____

_____

How can I apply these lessons in my life?_____

_____

_____

_____

_____

_____

What am I going to achieve today?

_____

_____

_____

_____

My Two Minute Journal

Date: _____

Evening:

What was my biggest challenge today?_____

_____

_____

What did I learn about myself from this challenge? _____

_____

_____

How can I apply this lesson in my life?_____

_____

_____

_____

_____

What can I do to make tomorrow better than today?

_____

_____

_____

_____

My Two Minute Journal

Date: _____

Morning:

What did I learn while I slept/dreamed?

_____

_____

_____

_____

_____

How can I apply these lessons in my life?_____

_____

_____

_____

_____

_____

What am I going to achieve today?

_____

_____

_____

_____

My Two Minute Journal

Date: _____

Evening:

What was my biggest challenge today?_____

_____

_____

What did I learn about myself from this challenge? _____

_____

_____

How can I apply this lesson in my life?_____

_____

_____

_____

_____

What can I do to make tomorrow better than today?

_____

_____

_____

_____

My Two Minute Journal

Date: _____

Morning:

What did I learn while I slept/dreamed?

_____

_____

_____

_____

_____

How can I apply these lessons in my life?_____

_____

_____

_____

_____

_____

What am I going to achieve today?

_____

_____

_____

_____

My Two Minute Journal

Date: _____

Weekly Review

As I review my week, I notice these recurring
themes/events/thoughts: _____

_____

_____

_____

_____

The lesson for me to learn in this cycle is: _____

_____

_____

_____

To break the cycle and move forward, I am going to change
my actions in this way: _____

_____

_____

_____

_____

"Success is the sum of small efforts, repeated day-in and day-out."

~ Robert Collier

My Two Minute Journal

Date: _____

Evening:

What was my biggest challenge today?_____

_____

_____

What did I learn about myself from this challenge? _____

_____

_____

How can I apply this lesson in my life?_____

_____

_____

_____

_____

What can I do to make tomorrow better than today?

_____

_____

_____

_____

My Two Minute Journal

Date: _____

Morning:

What did I learn while I slept/dreamed?

_____

_____

_____

_____

_____

How can I apply these lessons in my life?_____

_____

_____

_____

_____

_____

What am I going to achieve today?

_____

_____

_____

_____

My Two Minute Journal

Date: _____

Evening:

What was my biggest challenge today?_____

_____

_____

What did I learn about myself from this challenge? _____

_____

_____

How can I apply this lesson in my life?_____

_____

_____

_____

_____

What can I do to make tomorrow better than today?

_____

_____

_____

_____

My Two Minute Journal

Date: _____

Morning:

What did I learn while I slept/dreamed?

_____

_____

_____

_____

_____

How can I apply these lessons in my life?_____

_____

_____

_____

_____

_____

What am I going to achieve today?

_____

_____

_____

_____

My Two Minute Journal

Date: _____

Evening:

What was my biggest challenge today?_____

_____

_____

What did I learn about myself from this challenge? _____

_____

_____

How can I apply this lesson in my life?_____

_____

_____

_____

_____

What can I do to make tomorrow better than today?

_____

_____

_____

_____

My Two Minute Journal

Date: _____

Morning:

What did I learn while I slept/dreamed?

_____

_____

_____

_____

_____

How can I apply these lessons in my life?_____

_____

_____

_____

_____

_____

What am I going to achieve today?

_____

_____

_____

_____

My Two Minute Journal

Date: _____

Evening:

What was my biggest challenge today?_____

_____

_____

What did I learn about myself from this challenge? _____

_____

_____

How can I apply this lesson in my life?_____

_____

_____

_____

_____

What can I do to make tomorrow better than today?

_____

_____

_____

_____

My Two Minute Journal

Date: _____

Morning:

What did I learn while I slept/dreamed?

_____

_____

_____

_____

_____

How can I apply these lessons in my life?_____

_____

_____

_____

_____

_____

What am I going to achieve today?

_____

_____

_____

_____

My Two Minute Journal

Date: _____

Evening:

What was my biggest challenge today? _____

_____

_____

What did I learn about myself from this challenge? _____

_____

_____

How can I apply this lesson in my life? _____

_____

_____

_____

_____

What can I do to make tomorrow better than today?

_____

_____

_____

_____

My Two Minute Journal

Date: _____

Morning:

What did I learn while I slept/dreamed?

_____

_____

_____

_____

_____

How can I apply these lessons in my life?_____

_____

_____

_____

_____

_____

What am I going to achieve today?

_____

_____

_____

_____

My Two Minute Journal

Date: _____

Evening:

What was my biggest challenge today?_____

_____

_____

What did I learn about myself from this challenge? _____

_____

_____

How can I apply this lesson in my life?_____

_____

_____

_____

_____

What can I do to make tomorrow better than today?

_____

_____

_____

_____

My Two Minute Journal

Date: _____

Morning:

What did I learn while I slept/dreamed?

_____

_____

_____

_____

_____

How can I apply these lessons in my life?_____

_____

_____

_____

_____

_____

What am I going to achieve today?

_____

_____

_____

_____

My Two Minute Journal

Date: _____

Evening:

What was my biggest challenge today? _____

_____

_____

What did I learn about myself from this challenge? _____

_____

_____

How can I apply this lesson in my life? _____

_____

_____

_____

_____

What can I do to make tomorrow better than today?

_____

_____

_____

_____

My Two Minute Journal

Date: _____

Morning:

What did I learn while I slept/dreamed?

_____

_____

_____

_____

_____

How can I apply these lessons in my life?_____

_____

_____

_____

_____

_____

What am I going to achieve today?

_____

_____

_____

_____

Date: _____

Weekly Review

As I review my week, I notice these recurring
themes/events/thoughts: _____

_____

_____

_____

_____

The lesson for me to learn in this cycle is: _____

_____

_____

_____

To break the cycle and move forward, I am going to change
my actions in this way: _____

_____

_____

_____

_____

"What seems to us as bitter trials are often blessings in disguise."

~ Oscar Wilde

My Two Minute Journal

Date: _____

Evening:

What was my biggest challenge today?_____

_____

_____

What did I learn about myself from this challenge? _____

_____

_____

How can I apply this lesson in my life?_____

_____

_____

_____

_____

What can I do to make tomorrow better than today?

_____

_____

_____

_____

My Two Minute Journal

Date: _____

Morning:

What did I learn while I slept/dreamed?

_____

_____

_____

_____

_____

How can I apply these lessons in my life?_____

_____

_____

_____

_____

_____

What am I going to achieve today?

_____

_____

_____

_____

My Two Minute Journal

Date: _____

Evening:

What was my biggest challenge today? _____

_____

_____

What did I learn about myself from this challenge? _____

_____

_____

How can I apply this lesson in my life? _____

_____

_____

_____

_____

What can I do to make tomorrow better than today?

_____

_____

_____

_____

My Two Minute Journal

Date: _____

Morning:

What did I learn while I slept/dreamed?

_____

_____

_____

_____

_____

How can I apply these lessons in my life?_____

_____

_____

_____

_____

_____

What am I going to achieve today?

_____

_____

_____

_____

My Two Minute Journal

Date: _____

Evening:

What was my biggest challenge today? _____

_____

_____

What did I learn about myself from this challenge? _____

_____

_____

How can I apply this lesson in my life? _____

_____

_____

_____

_____

What can I do to make tomorrow better than today?

_____

_____

_____

_____

My Two Minute Journal

Date: _____

Morning:

What did I learn while I slept/dreamed?

_____

_____

_____

_____

_____

How can I apply these lessons in my life?_____

_____

_____

_____

_____

_____

What am I going to achieve today?

_____

_____

_____

_____

My Two Minute Journal

Date: _____

Evening:

What was my biggest challenge today?_____

_____

_____

What did I learn about myself from this challenge? _____

_____

_____

How can I apply this lesson in my life?_____

_____

_____

_____

_____

What can I do to make tomorrow better than today?

_____

_____

_____

_____

My Two Minute Journal

Date: _____

Morning:

What did I learn while I slept/dreamed?

_____

_____

_____

_____

_____

How can I apply these lessons in my life?_____

_____

_____

_____

_____

_____

What am I going to achieve today?

_____

_____

_____

_____

My Two Minute Journal

Date: _____

Evening:

What was my biggest challenge today?_____

_____

_____

What did I learn about myself from this challenge? _____

_____

_____

How can I apply this lesson in my life?_____

_____

_____

_____

_____

What can I do to make tomorrow better than today?

_____

_____

_____

_____

My Two Minute Journal

Date: _____

Morning:

What did I learn while I slept/dreamed?

_____

_____

_____

_____

_____

How can I apply these lessons in my life?_____

_____

_____

_____

_____

_____

What am I going to achieve today?

_____

_____

_____

_____

My Two Minute Journal

Date: _____

Evening:

What was my biggest challenge today? _____

_____

_____

What did I learn about myself from this challenge? _____

_____

_____

How can I apply this lesson in my life? _____

_____

_____

_____

_____

What can I do to make tomorrow better than today?

_____

_____

_____

_____

My Two Minute Journal

Date: _____

Morning:

What did I learn while I slept/dreamed?

_____

_____

_____

_____

_____

How can I apply these lessons in my life?_____

_____

_____

_____

_____

_____

What am I going to achieve today?

_____

_____

_____

_____

My Two Minute Journal

Date: _____

Evening:

What was my biggest challenge today?_____

_____

_____

What did I learn about myself from this challenge? _____

_____

_____

How can I apply this lesson in my life?_____

_____

_____

_____

_____

What can I do to make tomorrow better than today?

_____

_____

_____

_____

My Two Minute Journal

Date: _____

Morning:

What did I learn while I slept/dreamed?

_____

_____

_____

_____

_____

How can I apply these lessons in my life?_____

_____

_____

_____

_____

_____

What am I going to achieve today?

_____

_____

_____

_____

Date: _____

Weekly Review

As I review my week, I notice these recurring
themes/events/thoughts: _____

_____

_____

_____

_____

The lesson for me to learn in this cycle is: _____

_____

_____

_____

To break the cycle and move forward, I am going to change
my actions in this way: _____

_____

_____

_____

_____

"Be patient with yourself. Self-growth is tender; it's holy ground. There's no greater investment."

~ Stephen Covey

My Two Minute Journal

Date: _____

Evening:

What was my biggest challenge today?_____

_____

_____

What did I learn about myself from this challenge? _____

_____

_____

How can I apply this lesson in my life?_____

_____

_____

_____

_____

What can I do to make tomorrow better than today?

_____

_____

_____

_____

My Two Minute Journal

Date: _____

Morning:

What did I learn while I slept/dreamed?

_____

_____

_____

_____

_____

How can I apply these lessons in my life?_____

_____

_____

_____

_____

_____

What am I going to achieve today?

_____

_____

_____

_____

My Two Minute Journal

Date: _____

Evening:

What was my biggest challenge today?_____

_____

_____

What did I learn about myself from this challenge? _____

_____

_____

How can I apply this lesson in my life?_____

_____

_____

_____

_____

What can I do to make tomorrow better than today?

_____

_____

_____

_____

My Two Minute Journal

Date: _____

Morning:

What did I learn while I slept/dreamed?

_____

_____

_____

_____

_____

How can I apply these lessons in my life?_____

_____

_____

_____

_____

_____

What am I going to achieve today?

_____

_____

_____

_____

My Two Minute Journal

Date: _____

Evening:

What was my biggest challenge today? _____

_____

_____

What did I learn about myself from this challenge? _____

_____

_____

How can I apply this lesson in my life? _____

_____

_____

_____

_____

What can I do to make tomorrow better than today?

_____

_____

_____

_____

My Two Minute Journal

Date: _____

Morning:

What did I learn while I slept/dreamed?

_____

_____

_____

_____

_____

How can I apply these lessons in my life?_____

_____

_____

_____

_____

_____

What am I going to achieve today?

_____

_____

_____

_____

My Two Minute Journal

Date: _____

Evening:

What was my biggest challenge today? _____

_____

_____

What did I learn about myself from this challenge? _____

_____

_____

How can I apply this lesson in my life? _____

_____

_____

_____

_____

What can I do to make tomorrow better than today?

_____

_____

_____

_____

My Two Minute Journal

Date: _____

Morning:

What did I learn while I slept/dreamed?

_____

_____

_____

_____

_____

How can I apply these lessons in my life?_____

_____

_____

_____

_____

_____

What am I going to achieve today?

_____

_____

_____

_____

My Two Minute Journal

Date: _____

Evening:

What was my biggest challenge today?_____

_____

_____

What did I learn about myself from this challenge? _____

_____

_____

How can I apply this lesson in my life?_____

_____

_____

_____

_____

What can I do to make tomorrow better than today?

_____

_____

_____

_____

My Two Minute Journal

Date: _____

Morning:

What did I learn while I slept/dreamed?

_____

_____

_____

_____

_____

How can I apply these lessons in my life?_____

_____

_____

_____

_____

_____

What am I going to achieve today?

_____

_____

_____

_____

My Two Minute Journal

Date: _____

Evening:

What was my biggest challenge today?_____

_____

_____

What did I learn about myself from this challenge? _____

_____

_____

How can I apply this lesson in my life?_____

_____

_____

_____

_____

What can I do to make tomorrow better than today?

_____

_____

_____

_____

My Two Minute Journal

Date: _____

Morning:

What did I learn while I slept/dreamed?

_____

_____

_____

_____

_____

How can I apply these lessons in my life?_____

_____

_____

_____

_____

_____

What am I going to achieve today?

_____

_____

_____

_____

My Two Minute Journal

Date: _____

Evening:

What was my biggest challenge today? _____

_____

_____

What did I learn about myself from this challenge? _____

_____

_____

How can I apply this lesson in my life? _____

_____

_____

_____

_____

What can I do to make tomorrow better than today?

_____

_____

_____

_____

Date: _____

Morning:

What did I learn while I slept/dreamed?

_____

_____

_____

_____

_____

How can I apply these lessons in my life?_____

_____

_____

_____

_____

_____

What am I going to achieve today?

_____

_____

_____

_____

Date: _____

Weekly Review

As I review my week, I notice these recurring themes/events/thoughts: _____

_____

_____

_____

_____

The lesson for me to learn in this cycle is: _____

_____

_____

_____

To break the cycle and move forward, I am going to change my actions in this way: _____

_____

_____

_____

_____

"Courage is resistance to fear,
mastery of fear--
not absence of fear."

~ Mark Twain

Date: _____

Monthly Review

As I review my past 4 weeks, I notice these recurring themes/events/thoughts: _____

_____

_____

_____

_____

As I notice these patterns, my biggest fear is: _____

_____

_____

_____

What is waiting for me on the other side of the fear? _____

_____

_____

_____

_____

Date: _____

Monthly Review

Why has it been important for me up until now to continue these actions that do not serve my long-term achievement?

_____

_____

_____

_____

What do I need to do differently to achieve my goals? _____

_____

_____

_____

I now commit to the following action/goal in the next 28 days: _____

_____

_____

_____

My Two Minute Journal

"Don't be afraid to give up the good to go for the great."

~ *John D. Rockefeller*

My Two Minute Journal

Date: _____

Evening:

What was my biggest challenge today?_____

_____

_____

What did I learn about myself from this challenge? _____

_____

_____

How can I apply this lesson in my life?_____

_____

_____

_____

_____

What can I do to make tomorrow better than today?

_____

_____

_____

_____

My Two Minute Journal

Date: _____

Morning:

What did I learn while I slept/dreamed?

_____

_____

_____

_____

_____

How can I apply these lessons in my life?_____

_____

_____

_____

_____

_____

What am I going to achieve today?

_____

_____

_____

_____

My Two Minute Journal

Date: _____

Evening:

What was my biggest challenge today?_____

_____

_____

What did I learn about myself from this challenge? _____

_____

_____

How can I apply this lesson in my life?_____

_____

_____

_____

_____

What can I do to make tomorrow better than today?

_____

_____

_____

_____

My Two Minute Journal

Date: _____

Morning:

What did I learn while I slept/dreamed?

_____

_____

_____

_____

_____

How can I apply these lessons in my life?_____

_____

_____

_____

_____

_____

What am I going to achieve today?

_____

_____

_____

_____

My Two Minute Journal

Date: _____

Evening:

What was my biggest challenge today? _____

_____

_____

What did I learn about myself from this challenge? _____

_____

_____

How can I apply this lesson in my life? _____

_____

_____

_____

_____

What can I do to make tomorrow better than today?

_____

_____

_____

_____

My Two Minute Journal

Date: _____

Morning:

What did I learn while I slept/dreamed?

_____

_____

_____

_____

_____

How can I apply these lessons in my life?_____

_____

_____

_____

_____

_____

What am I going to achieve today?

_____

_____

_____

_____

My Two Minute Journal

Date: _____

Evening:

What was my biggest challenge today?_____

_____

_____

What did I learn about myself from this challenge? _____

_____

_____

How can I apply this lesson in my life?_____

_____

_____

_____

_____

What can I do to make tomorrow better than today?

_____

_____

_____

_____

My Two Minute Journal

Date: _____

Morning:

What did I learn while I slept/dreamed?

_____

_____

_____

_____

_____

How can I apply these lessons in my life?_____

_____

_____

_____

_____

_____

What am I going to achieve today?

_____

_____

_____

_____

My Two Minute Journal

Date: _____

Evening:

What was my biggest challenge today?_____

_____

_____

What did I learn about myself from this challenge? _____

_____

_____

How can I apply this lesson in my life?_____

_____

_____

_____

_____

What can I do to make tomorrow better than today?

_____

_____

_____

_____

My Two Minute Journal

Date: _____

Morning:

What did I learn while I slept/dreamed?

_____

_____

_____

_____

_____

How can I apply these lessons in my life?_____

_____

_____

_____

_____

_____

What am I going to achieve today?

_____

_____

_____

_____

My Two Minute Journal

Date: _____

Evening:

What was my biggest challenge today? _____

_____

_____

What did I learn about myself from this challenge? _____

_____

_____

How can I apply this lesson in my life? _____

_____

_____

_____

_____

What can I do to make tomorrow better than today?

_____

_____

_____

_____

My Two Minute Journal

Date: _____

Morning:

What did I learn while I slept/dreamed?

_____

_____

_____

_____

_____

How can I apply these lessons in my life?_____

_____

_____

_____

_____

_____

What am I going to achieve today?

_____

_____

_____

_____

My Two Minute Journal

Date: _____

Evening:

What was my biggest challenge today?_____

_____

_____

What did I learn about myself from this challenge? _____

_____

_____

How can I apply this lesson in my life?_____

_____

_____

_____

_____

What can I do to make tomorrow better than today?

_____

_____

_____

_____

My Two Minute Journal

Date: _____

Morning:

What did I learn while I slept/dreamed?

_____

_____

_____

_____

_____

How can I apply these lessons in my life?_____

_____

_____

_____

_____

_____

What am I going to achieve today?

_____

_____

_____

_____

Date: _____

Weekly Review

As I review my week, I notice these recurring
themes/events/thoughts: _____

_____

_____

_____

_____

The lesson for me to learn in this cycle is: _____

_____

_____

_____

To break the cycle and move forward, I am going to change
my actions in this way: _____

_____

_____

_____

_____

"All our dreams can come true if we have the courage to pursue them."

~ Walt Disney

My Two Minute Journal

Date: _____

Evening:

What was my biggest challenge today? _____

_____

_____

What did I learn about myself from this challenge? _____

_____

_____

How can I apply this lesson in my life?_____

_____

_____

_____

_____

What can I do to make tomorrow better than today?

_____

_____

_____

_____

My Two Minute Journal

Date: _____

Morning:

What did I learn while I slept/dreamed?

_____

_____

_____

_____

_____

How can I apply these lessons in my life?_____

_____

_____

_____

_____

_____

What am I going to achieve today?

_____

_____

_____

_____

My Two Minute Journal

Date: _____

Evening:

What was my biggest challenge today?_____

_____

_____

What did I learn about myself from this challenge? _____

_____

_____

How can I apply this lesson in my life?_____

_____

_____

_____

_____

What can I do to make tomorrow better than today?

_____

_____

_____

_____

My Two Minute Journal

Date: _____

Morning:

What did I learn while I slept/dreamed?

_____

_____

_____

_____

_____

How can I apply these lessons in my life?_____

_____

_____

_____

_____

_____

What am I going to achieve today?

_____

_____

_____

_____

My Two Minute Journal

Date: _____

Evening:

What was my biggest challenge today?_____

_____

_____

What did I learn about myself from this challenge? _____

_____

_____

How can I apply this lesson in my life?_____

_____

_____

_____

_____

What can I do to make tomorrow better than today?

_____

_____

_____

_____

My Two Minute Journal

Date: _____

Morning:

What did I learn while I slept/dreamed?

_____

_____

_____

_____

_____

How can I apply these lessons in my life?_____

_____

_____

_____

_____

_____

What am I going to achieve today?

_____

_____

_____

_____

My Two Minute Journal

Date: _____

Evening:

What was my biggest challenge today?_____

_____

_____

What did I learn about myself from this challenge? _____

_____

_____

How can I apply this lesson in my life?_____

_____

_____

_____

_____

What can I do to make tomorrow better than today?

_____

_____

_____

_____

My Two Minute Journal

Date: _____

Morning:

What did I learn while I slept/dreamed?

_____

_____

_____

_____

_____

How can I apply these lessons in my life?_____

_____

_____

_____

_____

_____

What am I going to achieve today?

_____

_____

_____

_____

My Two Minute Journal

Date: _____

Evening:

What was my biggest challenge today?_____

_____

_____

What did I learn about myself from this challenge? _____

_____

_____

How can I apply this lesson in my life?_____

_____

_____

_____

_____

What can I do to make tomorrow better than today?

_____

_____

_____

_____

My Two Minute Journal

Date: _____

Morning:

What did I learn while I slept/dreamed?

_____

_____

_____

_____

_____

How can I apply these lessons in my life?_____

_____

_____

_____

_____

_____

What am I going to achieve today?

_____

_____

_____

_____

My Two Minute Journal

Date: _____

Evening:

What was my biggest challenge today? _____

_____

_____

What did I learn about myself from this challenge? _____

_____

_____

How can I apply this lesson in my life? _____

_____

_____

_____

_____

What can I do to make tomorrow better than today?

_____

_____

_____

_____

My Two Minute Journal

Date: _____

Morning:

What did I learn while I slept/dreamed?

_____

_____

_____

_____

_____

How can I apply these lessons in my life?_____

_____

_____

_____

_____

_____

What am I going to achieve today?

_____

_____

_____

_____

My Two Minute Journal

Date: _____

Evening:

What was my biggest challenge today?_____

_____

_____

What did I learn about myself from this challenge? _____

_____

_____

How can I apply this lesson in my life?_____

_____

_____

_____

_____

What can I do to make tomorrow better than today?

_____

_____

_____

_____

My Two Minute Journal

Date: _____

Morning:

What did I learn while I slept/dreamed?

_____

_____

_____

_____

_____

How can I apply these lessons in my life?_____

_____

_____

_____

_____

_____

What am I going to achieve today?

_____

_____

_____

_____

Date: _____

Weekly Review

As I review my week, I notice these recurring themes/events/thoughts: _____

_____

_____

_____

_____

The lesson for me to learn in this cycle is: _____

_____

_____

_____

To break the cycle and move forward, I am going to change my actions in this way: _____

_____

_____

_____

_____

"If you are willing to do more than you are paid to do, eventually you will be paid to do more than you do."

~ *Anonymous*

My Two Minute Journal

Date: _____

Evening:

What was my biggest challenge today?_____

_____

_____

What did I learn about myself from this challenge? _____

_____

_____

How can I apply this lesson in my life?_____

_____

_____

_____

_____

What can I do to make tomorrow better than today?

_____

_____

_____

_____

My Two Minute Journal

Date: _____

Morning:

What did I learn while I slept/dreamed?

_____

_____

_____

_____

_____

How can I apply these lessons in my life?_____

_____

_____

_____

_____

_____

What am I going to achieve today?

_____

_____

_____

_____

My Two Minute Journal

Date: _____

Evening:

What was my biggest challenge today? _____

_____

_____

What did I learn about myself from this challenge? _____

_____

_____

How can I apply this lesson in my life? _____

_____

_____

_____

_____

What can I do to make tomorrow better than today?

_____

_____

_____

_____

My Two Minute Journal

Date: _____

Morning:

What did I learn while I slept/dreamed?

_____

_____

_____

_____

_____

How can I apply these lessons in my life?_____

_____

_____

_____

_____

_____

What am I going to achieve today?

_____

_____

_____

_____

My Two Minute Journal

Date: _____

Evening:

What was my biggest challenge today?_____

_____

_____

What did I learn about myself from this challenge? _____

_____

_____

How can I apply this lesson in my life?_____

_____

_____

_____

_____

What can I do to make tomorrow better than today?

_____

_____

_____

_____

My Two Minute Journal

Date: _____

Morning:

What did I learn while I slept/dreamed?

_____

_____

_____

_____

_____

How can I apply these lessons in my life?_____

_____

_____

_____

_____

_____

What am I going to achieve today?

_____

_____

_____

_____

My Two Minute Journal

Date: _____

Evening:

What was my biggest challenge today? _____

_____

_____

What did I learn about myself from this challenge? _____

_____

_____

How can I apply this lesson in my life? _____

_____

_____

_____

_____

What can I do to make tomorrow better than today?

_____

_____

_____

_____

My Two Minute Journal

Date: _____

Morning:

What did I learn while I slept/dreamed?

_____

_____

_____

_____

_____

How can I apply these lessons in my life?_____

_____

_____

_____

_____

_____

What am I going to achieve today?

_____

_____

_____

_____

My Two Minute Journal

Date: _____

Evening:

What was my biggest challenge today?_____

_____

_____

What did I learn about myself from this challenge? _____

_____

_____

How can I apply this lesson in my life?_____

_____

_____

_____

_____

What can I do to make tomorrow better than today?

_____

_____

_____

_____

My Two Minute Journal

Date: _____

Morning:

What did I learn while I slept/dreamed?

_____

_____

_____

_____

_____

How can I apply these lessons in my life?_____

_____

_____

_____

_____

_____

What am I going to achieve today?

_____

_____

_____

_____

My Two Minute Journal

Date: _____

Evening:

What was my biggest challenge today?_____

_____

_____

What did I learn about myself from this challenge? _____

_____

_____

How can I apply this lesson in my life?_____

_____

_____

_____

_____

What can I do to make tomorrow better than today?

_____

_____

_____

_____

My Two Minute Journal

Date: _____

Morning:

What did I learn while I slept/dreamed?

_____

_____

_____

_____

_____

How can I apply these lessons in my life?_____

_____

_____

_____

_____

_____

What am I going to achieve today?

_____

_____

_____

_____

My Two Minute Journal

Date: _____

Evening:

What was my biggest challenge today?_____

_____

_____

What did I learn about myself from this challenge? _____

_____

_____

How can I apply this lesson in my life?_____

_____

_____

_____

_____

What can I do to make tomorrow better than today?

_____

_____

_____

_____

My Two Minute Journal

Date: _____

Morning:

What did I learn while I slept/dreamed?

_____

_____

_____

_____

_____

How can I apply these lessons in my life?_____

_____

_____

_____

_____

_____

What am I going to achieve today?

_____

_____

_____

_____

Date: _____

Weekly Review

As I review my week, I notice these recurring themes/events/thoughts: _____

_____

_____

_____

_____

The lesson for me to learn in this cycle is: _____

_____

_____

_____

To break the cycle and move forward, I am going to change my actions in this way: _____

_____

_____

_____

_____

"You miss 100% of the shots you don't take."

~ Wayne Gretzky

My Two Minute Journal

Date: _____

Evening:

What was my biggest challenge today?_____

_____

_____

What did I learn about myself from this challenge? _____

_____

_____

How can I apply this lesson in my life?_____

_____

_____

_____

_____

What can I do to make tomorrow better than today?

_____

_____

_____

_____

My Two Minute Journal

Date: _____

Morning:

What did I learn while I slept/dreamed?

_____

_____

_____

_____

_____

How can I apply these lessons in my life?_____

_____

_____

_____

_____

_____

What am I going to achieve today?

_____

_____

_____

_____

My Two Minute Journal

Date: _____

Evening:

What was my biggest challenge today? _____

_____

_____

What did I learn about myself from this challenge? _____

_____

_____

How can I apply this lesson in my life? _____

_____

_____

_____

_____

What can I do to make tomorrow better than today?

_____

_____

_____

_____

My Two Minute Journal

Date: _____

Morning:

What did I learn while I slept/dreamed?

_____

_____

_____

_____

_____

How can I apply these lessons in my life?_____

_____

_____

_____

_____

_____

What am I going to achieve today?

_____

_____

_____

_____

My Two Minute Journal

Date: _____

Evening:

What was my biggest challenge today?_____

_____

_____

What did I learn about myself from this challenge? _____

_____

_____

How can I apply this lesson in my life?_____

_____

_____

_____

_____

What can I do to make tomorrow better than today?

_____

_____

_____

_____

My Two Minute Journal

Date: _____

Morning:

What did I learn while I slept/dreamed?

_____

_____

_____

_____

_____

How can I apply these lessons in my life?_____

_____

_____

_____

_____

_____

What am I going to achieve today?

_____

_____

_____

_____

My Two Minute Journal

Date: _____

Evening:

What was my biggest challenge today?_____

_____

_____

What did I learn about myself from this challenge? _____

_____

_____

How can I apply this lesson in my life?_____

_____

_____

_____

_____

What can I do to make tomorrow better than today?

_____

_____

_____

_____

My Two Minute Journal

Date: _____

Morning:

What did I learn while I slept/dreamed?

_____

_____

_____

_____

_____

How can I apply these lessons in my life?_____

_____

_____

_____

_____

_____

What am I going to achieve today?

_____

_____

_____

_____

My Two Minute Journal

Date: _____

Evening:

What was my biggest challenge today?_____

_____

_____

What did I learn about myself from this challenge? _____

_____

_____

How can I apply this lesson in my life?_____

_____

_____

_____

_____

What can I do to make tomorrow better than today?

_____

_____

_____

_____

My Two Minute Journal

Date: _____

Morning:

What did I learn while I slept/dreamed?

_____

_____

_____

_____

_____

How can I apply these lessons in my life?_____

_____

_____

_____

_____

_____

What am I going to achieve today?

_____

_____

_____

_____

My Two Minute Journal

Date: _____

Evening:

What was my biggest challenge today? _____

_____

_____

What did I learn about myself from this challenge? _____

_____

_____

How can I apply this lesson in my life? _____

_____

_____

_____

_____

What can I do to make tomorrow better than today?

_____

_____

_____

_____

My Two Minute Journal

Date: _____

Morning:

What did I learn while I slept/dreamed?

_____

_____

_____

_____

_____

How can I apply these lessons in my life?_____

_____

_____

_____

_____

_____

What am I going to achieve today?

_____

_____

_____

_____

My Two Minute Journal

Date: _____

Evening:

What was my biggest challenge today? _____

_____

_____

What did I learn about myself from this challenge? _____

_____

_____

How can I apply this lesson in my life? _____

_____

_____

_____

_____

What can I do to make tomorrow better than today?

_____

_____

_____

_____

My Two Minute Journal

Date: _____

Morning:

What did I learn while I slept/dreamed?

_____

_____

_____

_____

_____

How can I apply these lessons in my life?_____

_____

_____

_____

_____

_____

What am I going to achieve today?

_____

_____

_____

_____

Date: _____

Weekly Review

As I review my week, I notice these recurring
themes/events/thoughts: _____

_____

_____

_____

_____

The lesson for me to learn in this cycle is: _____

_____

_____

_____

To break the cycle and move forward, I am going to change
my actions in this way: _____

_____

_____

_____

_____

"Twenty years from now you will be more disappointed by the things that you didn't do than by the ones you did do, so throw off the bowlines, sail away from safe harbor, catch the trade winds in your sails. Explore, Dream, Discover."

~ *Mark Twain*

Date: _____

Monthly Review

As I review my past 4 weeks, I notice these recurring themes/events/thoughts: _____

_____

_____

_____

_____

As I notice these patterns, my biggest fear is: _____

_____

_____

_____

What is waiting for me on the other side of the fear? _____

_____

_____

_____

_____

Date: _____

Monthly Review

Why has it been important for me up until now to continue these actions that do not serve my long-term achievement?

_____

_____

_____

_____

What do I need to do differently to achieve my goals? _____

_____

_____

_____

I now commit to the following action/goal in the next 28 days:_____

_____

_____

_____

My Two Minute Journal

"The most difficult thing is the decision to act, the rest is merely tenacity."

~ Amelia Earhart

My Two Minute Journal

Date: _____

Evening:

What was my biggest challenge today?_____

_____

_____

What did I learn about myself from this challenge? _____

_____

_____

How can I apply this lesson in my life?_____

_____

_____

_____

_____

What can I do to make tomorrow better than today?

_____

_____

_____

_____

My Two Minute Journal

Date: _____

Morning:

What did I learn while I slept/dreamed?

_____

_____

_____

_____

_____

How can I apply these lessons in my life?_____

_____

_____

_____

_____

_____

What am I going to achieve today?

_____

_____

_____

_____

My Two Minute Journal

Date: _____

Evening:

What was my biggest challenge today?_____

_____

_____

What did I learn about myself from this challenge? _____

_____

_____

How can I apply this lesson in my life?_____

_____

_____

_____

_____

What can I do to make tomorrow better than today?

_____

_____

_____

_____

My Two Minute Journal

Date: _____

Morning:

What did I learn while I slept/dreamed?

_____

_____

_____

_____

_____

How can I apply these lessons in my life?_____

_____

_____

_____

_____

_____

What am I going to achieve today?

_____

_____

_____

_____

My Two Minute Journal

Date: _____

Evening:

What was my biggest challenge today?_____

_____

_____

What did I learn about myself from this challenge? _____

_____

_____

How can I apply this lesson in my life?_____

_____

_____

_____

_____

What can I do to make tomorrow better than today?

_____

_____

_____

_____

My Two Minute Journal

Date: _____

Morning:

What did I learn while I slept/dreamed?

_____

_____

_____

_____

_____

How can I apply these lessons in my life?_____

_____

_____

_____

_____

_____

What am I going to achieve today?

_____

_____

_____

_____

My Two Minute Journal

Date: _____

Evening:

What was my biggest challenge today?_____

_____

_____

What did I learn about myself from this challenge? _____

_____

_____

How can I apply this lesson in my life?_____

_____

_____

_____

_____

What can I do to make tomorrow better than today?

_____

_____

_____

_____

My Two Minute Journal

Date: _____

Morning:

What did I learn while I slept/dreamed?

_____

_____

_____

_____

_____

How can I apply these lessons in my life?_____

_____

_____

_____

_____

_____

What am I going to achieve today?

_____

_____

_____

_____

My Two Minute Journal

Date: _____

Evening:

What was my biggest challenge today? _____

_____

_____

What did I learn about myself from this challenge? _____

_____

_____

How can I apply this lesson in my life? _____

_____

_____

_____

_____

What can I do to make tomorrow better than today?

_____

_____

_____

_____

My Two Minute Journal

Date: _____

Morning:

What did I learn while I slept/dreamed?

_____

_____

_____

_____

_____

How can I apply these lessons in my life?_____

_____

_____

_____

_____

_____

What am I going to achieve today?

_____

_____

_____

_____

My Two Minute Journal

Date: _____

Evening:

What was my biggest challenge today?_____

_____

_____

What did I learn about myself from this challenge? _____

_____

_____

How can I apply this lesson in my life?_____

_____

_____

_____

_____

What can I do to make tomorrow better than today?

_____

_____

_____

_____

My Two Minute Journal

Date: _____

Morning:

What did I learn while I slept/dreamed?

_____

_____

_____

_____

_____

How can I apply these lessons in my life?_____

_____

_____

_____

_____

_____

What am I going to achieve today?

_____

_____

_____

_____

My Two Minute Journal

Date: _____

Evening:

What was my biggest challenge today?_____

_____

_____

What did I learn about myself from this challenge? _____

_____

_____

How can I apply this lesson in my life?_____

_____

_____

_____

_____

What can I do to make tomorrow better than today?

_____

_____

_____

_____

My Two Minute Journal

Date: _____

Morning:

What did I learn while I slept/dreamed?

_____

_____

_____

_____

_____

How can I apply these lessons in my life?_____

_____

_____

_____

_____

_____

What am I going to achieve today?

_____

_____

_____

_____

Date: _____

Weekly Review

As I review my week, I notice these recurring
themes/events/thoughts: _____

_____

_____

_____

_____

The lesson for me to learn in this cycle is: _____

_____

_____

_____

To break the cycle and move forward, I am going to change
my actions in this way: _____

_____

_____

_____

_____

"The most common way people give up their power is by thinking they don't have any."

~ Alice Walker

My Two Minute Journal

Date: _____

Evening:

What was my biggest challenge today?_____

_____

_____

What did I learn about myself from this challenge? _____

_____

_____

How can I apply this lesson in my life?_____

_____

_____

_____

_____

What can I do to make tomorrow better than today?

_____

_____

_____

_____

My Two Minute Journal

Date: _____

Morning:

What did I learn while I slept/dreamed?

_____

_____

_____

_____

_____

How can I apply these lessons in my life?_____

_____

_____

_____

_____

_____

What am I going to achieve today?

_____

_____

_____

_____

My Two Minute Journal

Date: _____

Evening:

What was my biggest challenge today?_____

_____

_____

What did I learn about myself from this challenge? _____

_____

_____

How can I apply this lesson in my life?_____

_____

_____

_____

_____

What can I do to make tomorrow better than today?

_____

_____

_____

_____

My Two Minute Journal

Date: _____

Morning:

What did I learn while I slept/dreamed?

_____

_____

_____

_____

_____

How can I apply these lessons in my life?_____

_____

_____

_____

_____

_____

What am I going to achieve today?

_____

_____

_____

_____

My Two Minute Journal

Date: _____

Evening:

What was my biggest challenge today? _____

_____

_____

What did I learn about myself from this challenge? _____

_____

_____

How can I apply this lesson in my life? _____

_____

_____

_____

_____

What can I do to make tomorrow better than today?

_____

_____

_____

_____

My Two Minute Journal

Date: _____

Morning:

What did I learn while I slept/dreamed?

_____

_____

_____

_____

_____

How can I apply these lessons in my life?_____

_____

_____

_____

_____

_____

What am I going to achieve today?

_____

_____

_____

_____

My Two Minute Journal

Date: _____

Evening:

What was my biggest challenge today?_____

_____

_____

What did I learn about myself from this challenge? _____

_____

_____

How can I apply this lesson in my life?_____

_____

_____

_____

_____

What can I do to make tomorrow better than today?

_____

_____

_____

_____

My Two Minute Journal

Date: _____

Morning:

What did I learn while I slept/dreamed?

_____

_____

_____

_____

_____

How can I apply these lessons in my life?_____

_____

_____

_____

_____

_____

What am I going to achieve today?

_____

_____

_____

_____

My Two Minute Journal

Date: _____

Evening:

What was my biggest challenge today?_____

_____

_____

What did I learn about myself from this challenge? _____

_____

_____

How can I apply this lesson in my life?_____

_____

_____

_____

_____

What can I do to make tomorrow better than today?

_____

_____

_____

_____

My Two Minute Journal

Date: _____

Morning:

What did I learn while I slept/dreamed?

_____

_____

_____

_____

_____

How can I apply these lessons in my life?_____

_____

_____

_____

_____

_____

What am I going to achieve today?

_____

_____

_____

_____

My Two Minute Journal

Date: _____

Evening:

What was my biggest challenge today?_____

_____

_____

What did I learn about myself from this challenge? _____

_____

_____

How can I apply this lesson in my life?_____

_____

_____

_____

_____

What can I do to make tomorrow better than today?

_____

_____

_____

_____

My Two Minute Journal

Date: _____

Morning:

What did I learn while I slept/dreamed?

_____

_____

_____

_____

_____

How can I apply these lessons in my life?_____

_____

_____

_____

_____

_____

What am I going to achieve today?

_____

_____

_____

_____

My Two Minute Journal

Date: _____

Evening:

What was my biggest challenge today?_____

_____

_____

What did I learn about myself from this challenge? _____

_____

_____

How can I apply this lesson in my life?_____

_____

_____

_____

_____

What can I do to make tomorrow better than today?

_____

_____

_____

_____

My Two Minute Journal

Date: _____

Morning:

What did I learn while I slept/dreamed?

_____

_____

_____

_____

_____

How can I apply these lessons in my life?_____

_____

_____

_____

_____

_____

What am I going to achieve today?

_____

_____

_____

_____

Date: _____

Weekly Review

As I review my week, I notice these recurring
themes/events/thoughts: _____

_____

_____

_____

_____

The lesson for me to learn in this cycle is: _____

_____

_____

_____

To break the cycle and move forward, I am going to change
my actions in this way: _____

_____

_____

_____

_____

"The best time to plant a tree
was 20 years ago.
The second-best time is now."

~ Chinese Proverb

My Two Minute Journal

Date: _____

Evening:

What was my biggest challenge today? _____

_____

_____

What did I learn about myself from this challenge? _____

_____

_____

How can I apply this lesson in my life? _____

_____

_____

_____

_____

What can I do to make tomorrow better than today?

_____

_____

_____

_____

My Two Minute Journal

Date: _____

Morning:

What did I learn while I slept/dreamed?

_____

_____

_____

_____

_____

How can I apply these lessons in my life?_____

_____

_____

_____

_____

_____

What am I going to achieve today?

_____

_____

_____

_____

My Two Minute Journal

Date: _____

Evening:

What was my biggest challenge today?_____

_____

_____

What did I learn about myself from this challenge? _____

_____

_____

How can I apply this lesson in my life?_____

_____

_____

_____

_____

What can I do to make tomorrow better than today?

_____

_____

_____

_____

My Two Minute Journal

Date: _____

Morning:

What did I learn while I slept/dreamed?

_____

_____

_____

_____

_____

How can I apply these lessons in my life?_____

_____

_____

_____

_____

_____

What am I going to achieve today?

_____

_____

_____

_____

My Two Minute Journal

Date: _____

Evening:

What was my biggest challenge today?_____

_____

_____

What did I learn about myself from this challenge? _____

_____

_____

How can I apply this lesson in my life?_____

_____

_____

_____

_____

What can I do to make tomorrow better than today?

_____

_____

_____

_____

My Two Minute Journal

Date: _____

Morning:

What did I learn while I slept/dreamed?

_____

_____

_____

_____

_____

How can I apply these lessons in my life?_____

_____

_____

_____

_____

_____

What am I going to achieve today?

_____

_____

_____

_____

My Two Minute Journal

Date: _____

Evening:

What was my biggest challenge today? _____

_____

_____

What did I learn about myself from this challenge? _____

_____

_____

How can I apply this lesson in my life? _____

_____

_____

_____

_____

What can I do to make tomorrow better than today?

_____

_____

_____

_____

My Two Minute Journal

Date: _____

Morning:

What did I learn while I slept/dreamed?

_____

_____

_____

_____

_____

How can I apply these lessons in my life?_____

_____

_____

_____

_____

_____

What am I going to achieve today?

_____

_____

_____

_____

My Two Minute Journal

Date: _____

Evening:

What was my biggest challenge today?_____

_____

_____

What did I learn about myself from this challenge? _____

_____

_____

How can I apply this lesson in my life?_____

_____

_____

_____

_____

What can I do to make tomorrow better than today?

_____

_____

_____

_____

My Two Minute Journal

Date: _____

Morning:

What did I learn while I slept/dreamed?

_____

_____

_____

_____

_____

How can I apply these lessons in my life?_____

_____

_____

_____

_____

_____

What am I going to achieve today?

_____

_____

_____

_____

My Two Minute Journal

Date: _____

Evening:

What was my biggest challenge today?_____

_____

_____

What did I learn about myself from this challenge? _____

_____

_____

How can I apply this lesson in my life?_____

_____

_____

_____

_____

What can I do to make tomorrow better than today?

_____

_____

_____

_____

My Two Minute Journal

Date: _____

Morning:

What did I learn while I slept/dreamed?

_____

_____

_____

_____

_____

How can I apply these lessons in my life?_____

_____

_____

_____

_____

_____

What am I going to achieve today?

_____

_____

_____

_____

My Two Minute Journal

Date: _____

Evening:

What was my biggest challenge today? _____

_____

_____

What did I learn about myself from this challenge? _____

_____

_____

How can I apply this lesson in my life? _____

_____

_____

_____

_____

What can I do to make tomorrow better than today?

_____

_____

_____

_____

My Two Minute Journal

Date: _____

Morning:

What did I learn while I slept/dreamed?

_____

_____

_____

_____

_____

How can I apply these lessons in my life?_____

_____

_____

_____

_____

_____

What am I going to achieve today?

_____

_____

_____

_____

Date: _____

Weekly Review

As I review my week, I notice these recurring themes/events/thoughts: _____

_____

_____

_____

_____

The lesson for me to learn in this cycle is: _____

_____

_____

_____

To break the cycle and move forward, I am going to change my actions in this way: _____

_____

_____

_____

_____

"I am not a product of my circumstances.
I am a product of my decisions."

~ Stephen Covey

My Two Minute Journal

Date: _____

Evening:

What was my biggest challenge today?_____

_____

_____

What did I learn about myself from this challenge? _____

_____

_____

How can I apply this lesson in my life?_____

_____

_____

_____

_____

What can I do to make tomorrow better than today?

_____

_____

_____

_____

My Two Minute Journal

Date: _____

Morning:

What did I learn while I slept/dreamed?

_____

_____

_____

_____

_____

How can I apply these lessons in my life?_____

_____

_____

_____

_____

_____

What am I going to achieve today?

_____

_____

_____

_____

My Two Minute Journal

Date: _____

Evening:

What was my biggest challenge today? _____

_____

_____

What did I learn about myself from this challenge? _____

_____

_____

How can I apply this lesson in my life? _____

_____

_____

_____

_____

What can I do to make tomorrow better than today?

_____

_____

_____

_____

My Two Minute Journal

Date: _____

Morning:

What did I learn while I slept/dreamed?

_____

_____

_____

_____

_____

How can I apply these lessons in my life?_____

_____

_____

_____

_____

_____

What am I going to achieve today?

_____

_____

_____

_____

My Two Minute Journal

Date: _____

Evening:

What was my biggest challenge today? _____

_____

_____

What did I learn about myself from this challenge? _____

_____

_____

How can I apply this lesson in my life? _____

_____

_____

_____

_____

What can I do to make tomorrow better than today?

_____

_____

_____

_____

My Two Minute Journal

Date: _____

Morning:

What did I learn while I slept/dreamed?

_____

_____

_____

_____

_____

How can I apply these lessons in my life?_____

_____

_____

_____

_____

_____

What am I going to achieve today?

_____

_____

_____

_____

My Two Minute Journal

Date: _____

Evening:

What was my biggest challenge today?_____

_____

_____

What did I learn about myself from this challenge? _____

_____

_____

How can I apply this lesson in my life?_____

_____

_____

_____

_____

What can I do to make tomorrow better than today?

_____

_____

_____

_____

My Two Minute Journal

Date: _____

Morning:

What did I learn while I slept/dreamed?

_____

_____

_____

_____

_____

How can I apply these lessons in my life?_____

_____

_____

_____

_____

_____

What am I going to achieve today?

_____

_____

_____

_____

My Two Minute Journal

Date: _____

Evening:

What was my biggest challenge today? _____

_____

_____

What did I learn about myself from this challenge? _____

_____

_____

How can I apply this lesson in my life? _____

_____

_____

_____

_____

What can I do to make tomorrow better than today?

_____

_____

_____

_____

My Two Minute Journal

Date: _____

Morning:

What did I learn while I slept/dreamed?

_____

_____

_____

_____

_____

How can I apply these lessons in my life?_____

_____

_____

_____

_____

_____

What am I going to achieve today?

_____

_____

_____

_____

My Two Minute Journal

Date: _____

Evening:

What was my biggest challenge today?_____

_____

_____

What did I learn about myself from this challenge? _____

_____

_____

How can I apply this lesson in my life?_____

_____

_____

_____

_____

What can I do to make tomorrow better than today?

_____

_____

_____

_____

My Two Minute Journal

Date: _____

Morning:

What did I learn while I slept/dreamed?

_____

_____

_____

_____

_____

How can I apply these lessons in my life?_____

_____

_____

_____

_____

_____

What am I going to achieve today?

_____

_____

_____

_____

My Two Minute Journal

Date: _____

Evening:

What was my biggest challenge today?_____

_____

_____

What did I learn about myself from this challenge? _____

_____

_____

How can I apply this lesson in my life?_____

_____

_____

_____

_____

What can I do to make tomorrow better than today?

_____

_____

_____

_____

My Two Minute Journal

Date: _____

Morning:

What did I learn while I slept/dreamed?

_____

_____

_____

_____

_____

How can I apply these lessons in my life?_____

_____

_____

_____

_____

_____

What am I going to achieve today?

_____

_____

_____

_____

Date: _____

Weekly Review

As I review my week, I notice these recurring
themes/events/thoughts: _____

_____

_____

_____

_____

The lesson for me to learn in this cycle is: _____

_____

_____

_____

To break the cycle and move forward, I am going to change
my actions in this way: _____

_____

_____

_____

_____

*"Either you run the day,
or the day runs you."*

~ Jim Rohn

Date: _____

Monthly Review

As I review my past 4 weeks, I notice these recurring
themes/events/thoughts: _____

_____

_____

_____

_____

As I notice these patterns, my biggest fear is: _____

_____

_____

_____

What is waiting for me on the other side of the fear? _____

_____

_____

_____

_____

Date: _____

Monthly Review

Why has it been important for me up until now to continue
these actions that do not serve my long-term achievement?

_____

_____

_____

_____

What do I need to do differently to achieve my goals? _____

_____

_____

_____

I now commit to the following action/goal in the next 28
days:_____

_____

_____

_____

My Two Minute Journal

"Go confidently in the direction of your dreams. Live the life you have imagined."

~ Henry David Thoreau

My Two Minute Journal

About the Author

Daniel Olexa, CTHt, ACC is the co-author of Amazon #1 Bestsellers, *Practical Manifesting* and *A Pessimist's Guide to Manifesting*.

He leads international personal empowerment retreats and workshops with the intention of replacing limiting beliefs with awareness, connection, abundance, and infinite possibility, allowing participants to step into their big vision of life.

Currently based in Los Angeles, CA, Daniel transforms the lives of clients around the world through his unique approach to hypnotherapy and coaching.

For more information, visit him at www.danielolexa.com.

10294700R00125

Made in the USA
Monee, IL
26 August 2019